Tiny Tinkles Little Music

Little Performers
SHOW OFF
on the Black Keys

Created by **Debra Krol**   Pictures by **Corinne Orazietti & Melanie Hawkins**

This book is dedicated to
all the little people for inspiring me,
and all the BIG people for believing in me.

TIPS TO HELP YOU TEACH USING THIS BOOK

Welcome to the **Tiny Tinkles Little Musicians Series!**

This 4th book in the Little Performers Collection will teach your little musician how to easily identify ALL of the black key groups and combinations, and to find/play the black keys hands together in many different locations.

This book adds more complex multiple note combinations to help your child to grow more finger strength, dexterity and independence.

When playing the patterns and songs in this book, try to keep a very steady beat.

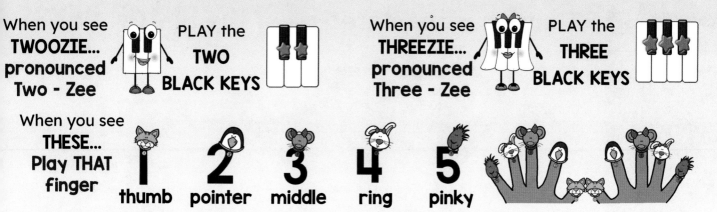

When you see **TWOOZIE...** pronounced Two - Zee / PLAY the **TWO** BLACK KEYS

When you see **THREEZIE...** pronounced Three - Zee / PLAY the **THREE** BLACK KEYS

When you see **THESE...** Play THAT finger

thumb 1   **pointer** 2   **middle** 3   **ring** 4   **pinky** 5

SING while you play the notes! Your little musician will FEEL the beat and rhythm of the music.

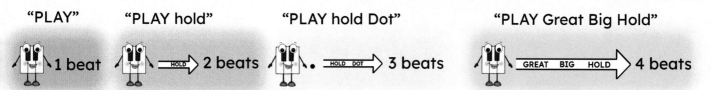

"PLAY" 1 beat

"PLAY hold" HOLD → 2 beats

"PLAY hold Dot" HOLD DOT → 3 beats

"PLAY Great Big Hold" GREAT BIG HOLD → 4 beats

TIPS TO HELP YOU PRACTICE AND LEARN TOGETHER

- Count slowly before you begin.
- Tap the notes and sing LEFT and RIGHT
- Circle patterns or common fingers
- Play and sing LEFT / RIGHT while you play
- Play and sing or the WORDS while you play
- Clap and Count the beat before you begin

For videos, worksheets, teaching tips and more... please visit: **www.tinytinkles.com**

Bobby Bass and Tina Treble are celebrating!

They have mastered all of the **BLACK KEYS.**

4

5

We can FIND and PLAY Twoozie's and Threezie's BLACK KEYs... **Can you?**

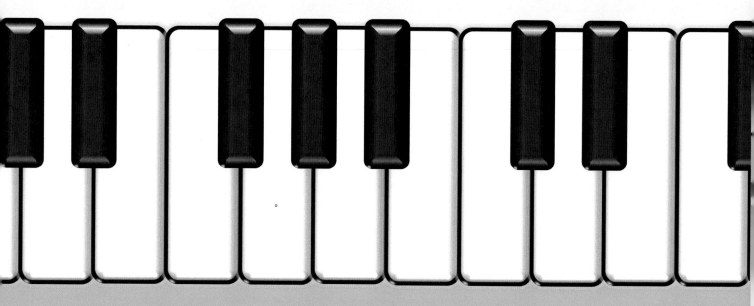

Ooooooo!

I can PLAY them **allegro FAST** like a **bat!**

Can you?

Yah!

And I can PLAY them **lento SLOW** like a butterfly!

Can you?

9

Oohhhhh

I can PLAY them down **LOW** and make them sound like a choo choo train... **Can you?**

Woo Hoo!

I can PLAY them up **HIGH** and make them sound like chirping birds... **Can you?**

We can play them **HANDS TOGETHER** with all sorts of fancy patterns!

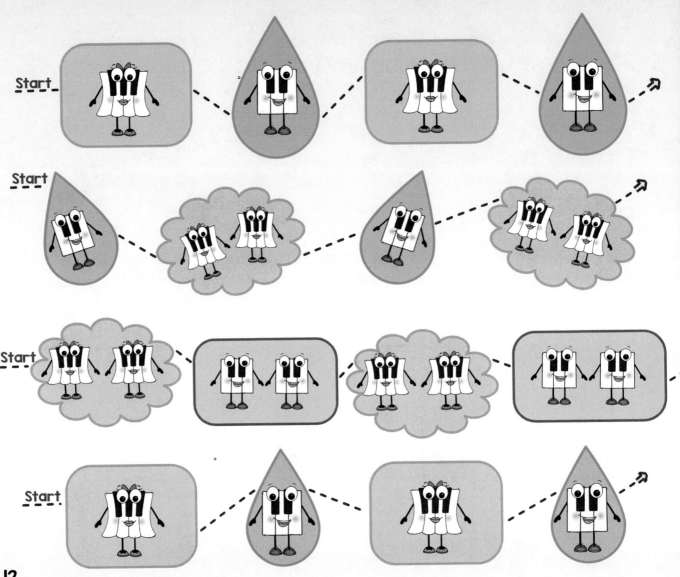

We will make our songs beautiful, with brilliant beginnings and amazing endings...

Maybe we should we make up our own fun melodies on the **2 Black Keys?**

Or... we could **flip** the pages and try these!

Little Owl

Li   ttle   owl   sings   hoot   hoot   hoot Hoot.

  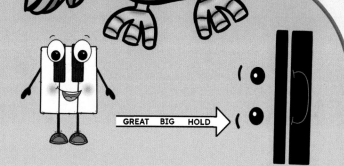

Li   ttle   owl   sings   Hoooooot!

GREAT BIG HOLD ➡

  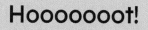

GREAT BIG HOLD ➡

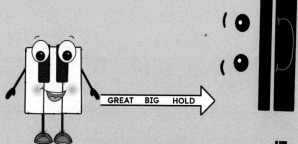

Sunshine

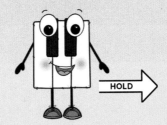

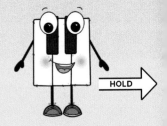

Let   her   shine,   let   her   shine.

18

Sun   shine,   shine   on   me.

Rocket Ship

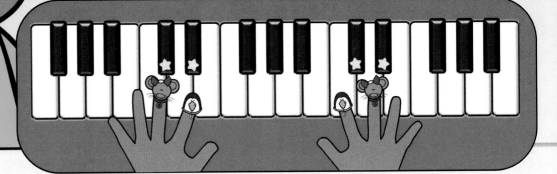

   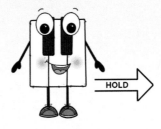

Ro   cket   ship,   ro   cket   ship.

  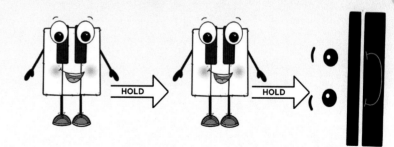

Start   your   en   gine,   BLAST   OFF!

    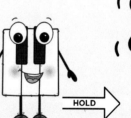 

Gobble, Gobble

 gob ble  gob ble

GLUCK!

 GREAT BIG HOLD →

 GREAT BIG HOLD →

Sing, Sing Violin!

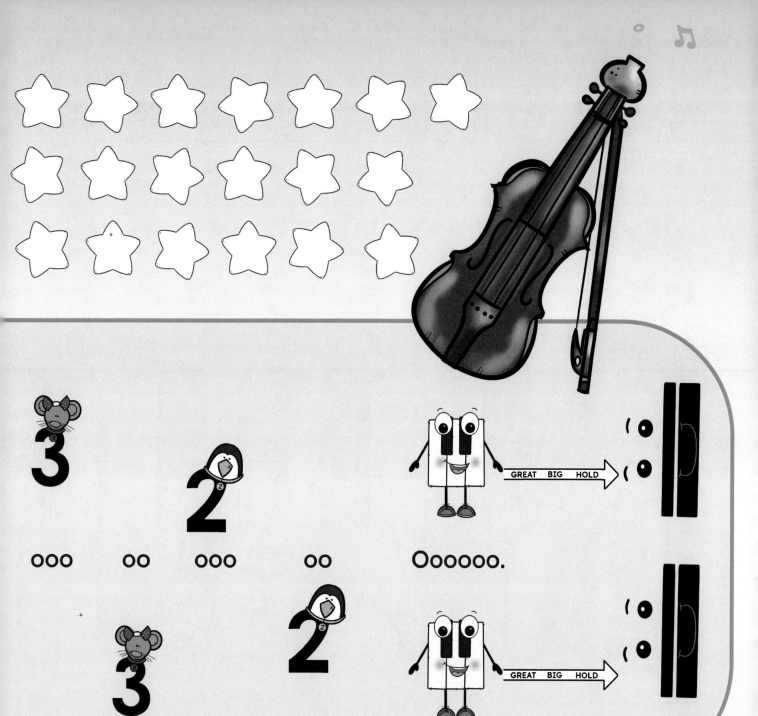

ooo   oo   ooo   oo   Oooooo.

GREAT BIG HOLD

GREAT BIG HOLD

25

Next... let's find the 3 black keys

Baby Birdie

Li ttle bir die, li ttle bir die,

28

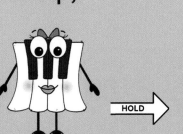 chirp,  chirp,  TWEET.

HOLD HOLD GREAT BIG HOLD

HOLD HOLD GREAT BIG HOLD

White Goose

My white goose loves to sing honk, honk, honk...

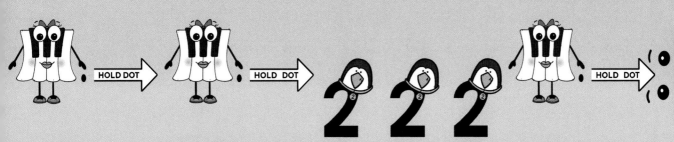

honk!   Honk!   Honk, honk, honk, honk!

BUZZY Mr. Fly

Buzz,   buzz,   buzz,   buzz,   fu   zzy

  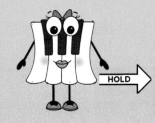  

3 3

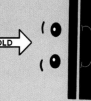

GREAT BIG HOLD →

black fly. Zzz Zzz Zzz Zzz Bzzzzzz!

GREAT BIG HOLD →

3 3

The World Spins

Round n' round   WEE!   round   n'   round WEE!

34

3 3 3

world keeps on

2 2 2

spin ning a

HOLD DOT

round.

3 3 3

2 2 2

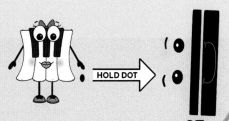

HOLD DOT

Jelly Beans!

Je   lly beans, YUM!

Je   lly beans,YUM!

36

I love to

eat je lly

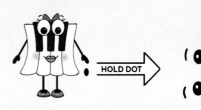
beans.

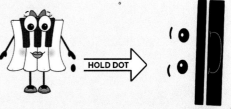

MIX it up and
find THIS hand position!

Which Groups MATCH?

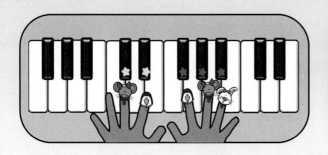

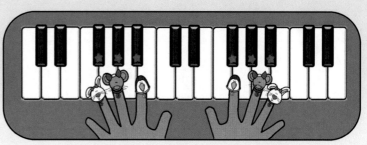

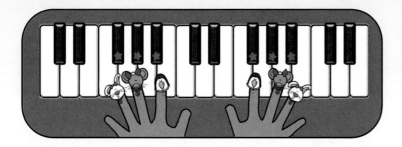

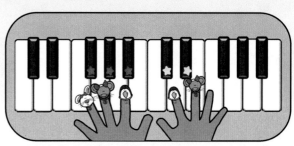

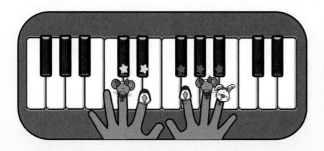

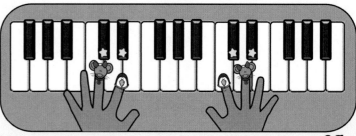

Hello Mr. Ant

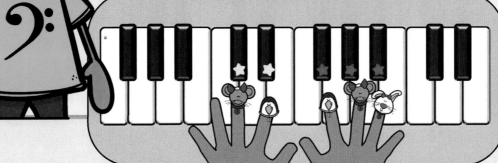

3 **3** **2** → HOLD

Mi ster Ant. Mi ster Ant. Hur rah!

3 **3** **2** → HOLD

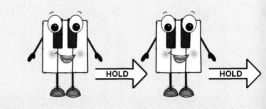

40

March ing, march ing, Mi ster Ant.

I can SKATE!

count
1 2 3 4

4 3 2 HOLD ➤ **4 3 2** HOLD ➤

I   can skate,   I   can skate.   Back and forth,

2 3 2 HOLD ➤

42

4 4
3 3
GREAT BIG HOLD

back and forth. Gli ding, gli ding, TWIRL...

2 2
3
HOLD

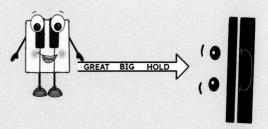

GREAT BIG HOLD

Bumble Bees

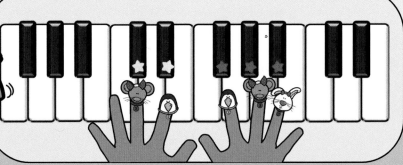

Buzz buzz bum ble bee...   Buzz buzz bum ble

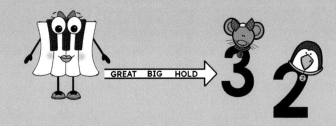

GREAT BIG HOLD

bee...   I   love   bum   ble   bees.

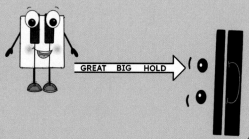

GREAT BIG HOLD

The Rainbow

Red, orange, ye llow...

Green, blue, pur ple...

Rain bows are

beau ti ful

things.

Wow... you know your KEYS!
Now, find these.

Which groups MATCH?

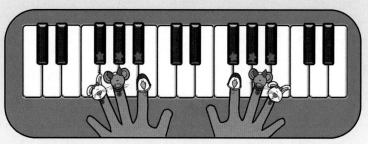

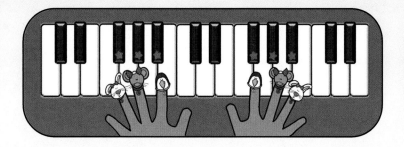

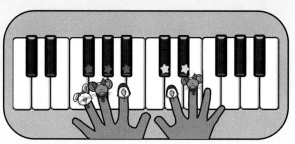

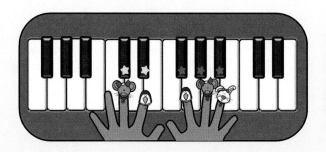

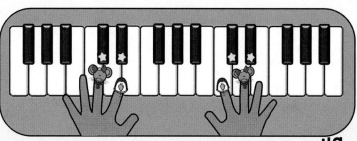

49

My Friend, Seagull

He llo friend, how are you?   I hear you

50

sing   ing...   tweet tweet tweet TWEET!

Night Night Time

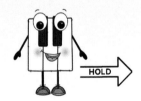

Sleep...   Sleep...   go   to   sleep...

52

 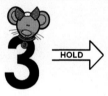 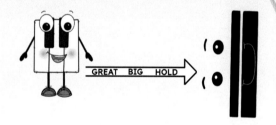

Shhh...   night night   time...   Sleep...

 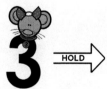 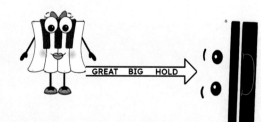

swir ling, swir ling, round and round and round...

Champions of the Black Keys

Woo   Hoo!   We   are   the   cham   pi   ons,

  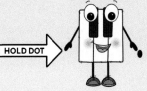

we   mas tered   all   of   the   BLACK   KEYS!

ABOUT THE CREATORS

Debra Krol is a BC Registered Music Teacher who specializes in teaching music to babies, toddlers and preschoolers. She is also a children's songwriter and author. Ms. Deb enjoys camping with her hubby, kids, and Daisy Dog, their black and tan coonhound. She loves playing piano, ukulele, guitar and most of all, singing & drawing with all of her little friends!

 Tiny Tinkles Music Studio tinytinkles

Corinne Orazietti was a preschool and elementary teacher for many years. She saw how her whimsical illustrations added sparkle to her lessons and decided it was time to share her passion for art with others. She now works as a full-time artist at her company, Chirp Graphics, and spends her days drawing cartoon dragons and fairies.

 chirpgraphics chirpgraphicsclipart

Melanie Hawkins is an author, illustrator, elementary art teacher and mom to seven children! Her family is her greatest source of joy and inspiration. She enjoys camping, swimming, dark chocolate, and movie nights with her family. Melanie is an eternal optimist and wishes that everyone could see the world as she does with all of its beauty, hope and goodness.

 melaniehawkinsauthor.com inspirejoypublishing

Love our Books?

We love hearing your stories!
Please visit our social media pages!
For all things Tiny Tinkles, visit
www.tinytinkles.com

CONGRATULATIONS!

_____

Student's Name

has completed Little Performers Level 4
in the Tiny Tinkles Little Musician Series.

LEVEL
4

_____

Teacher

_____

Date

Made in the°USA
Coppell, TX
01 October 2022

83914947R00036